WHERE'S BIDEN HIDEN?

Find Joe Biden in his Race to the White House

Illustrated By Theresa Vogrin

INTRODUCTION

Imagine that you are **Joe Biden.** You may not know that you are Joe Biden, but that's exactly what it's like to be Joe Biden. One moment you are snoozing peacefully on the Amtrak, the next you're flying a sheep through the land of Bedfordshire. Then, you suddenly wake up to find that you're about take on Trump in a one-to-one fight for the Presidency, but that's before you get a call from CNN. They're saying that a **thing** has just happened in Times Square, and they need you there to comment on it right away. What was that thing again? And what do they want you to do about it? None of that matters. What's important is that you find Ol' Joe as quickly as possible, so that he can get on top of the thing before it gets out of hand, whatever it is.

And now a word from Ol' uncle Joe himself:

> "This book has taken this year just since the outbreak, has taken more than 100 years – look, here's the time it's just it's just, I mean, think about it, more time this year than any other year for the past hundred years. C'mon man!"

What uncle Joe is trying to say here is that this book took a very long time to make.. so we really hope you enjoy it!

WHAT TO FIND ON EACH PAGE

On Every Page:

◯ Joe Biden (lookout for the white hair)

◯ 'Cup of Joe' mug

◯ Corn Pops

◯ Joe Bidens Sunglasses

◯ Joe Biden's sign language interpreter

◯ Hidden earpiece kit

◯ Ice Cream

◯ Teleprompter

1. Amtrak Joe

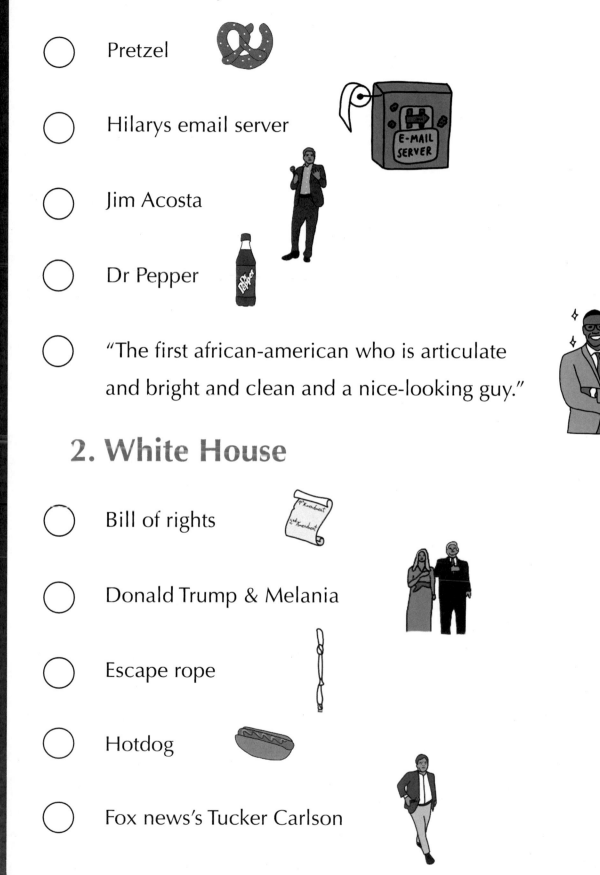

○ Pretzel

○ Hilarys email server

○ Jim Acosta

○ Dr Pepper

○ "The first african-american who is articulate and bright and clean and a nice-looking guy."

2. White House

○ Bill of rights

○ Donald Trump & Melania

○ Escape rope

○ Hotdog

○ Fox news's Tucker Carlson

3. Land of Bedfordshire

◯ Biden's pyjama hat

◯ CNN's Wolf Blitzer

◯ American flag

◯ Nuke

◯ Covid 19

4. Times Square

◯ Antifa graffiti x2   ACAB

◯ CNN's Don Lemon

◯ American flag

◯ LGBT Sign

◯ I heart communism shirt

5. Supreme Court

○ Bidens Corvette

○ Hillary behind bars

○ '#DO YOUR JOB' sign

○ Senator Mitch McConnel

○ Animal crackers

6. Trump Boat Parade

○ Antifa Flag

○ 10 american flags

○ American eagle

○ Red white and blue fish

○ MAGA cap

7. Wrestling Ring

○ CNN's Erin Burnett

○ American flag

○ John Cena

○ WWE belt

○ Paramedic

8. Beach

○ Rusty Razor

○ Bidens hairy legs

○ Roaches

○ Antifa flag

○ White house sand castle

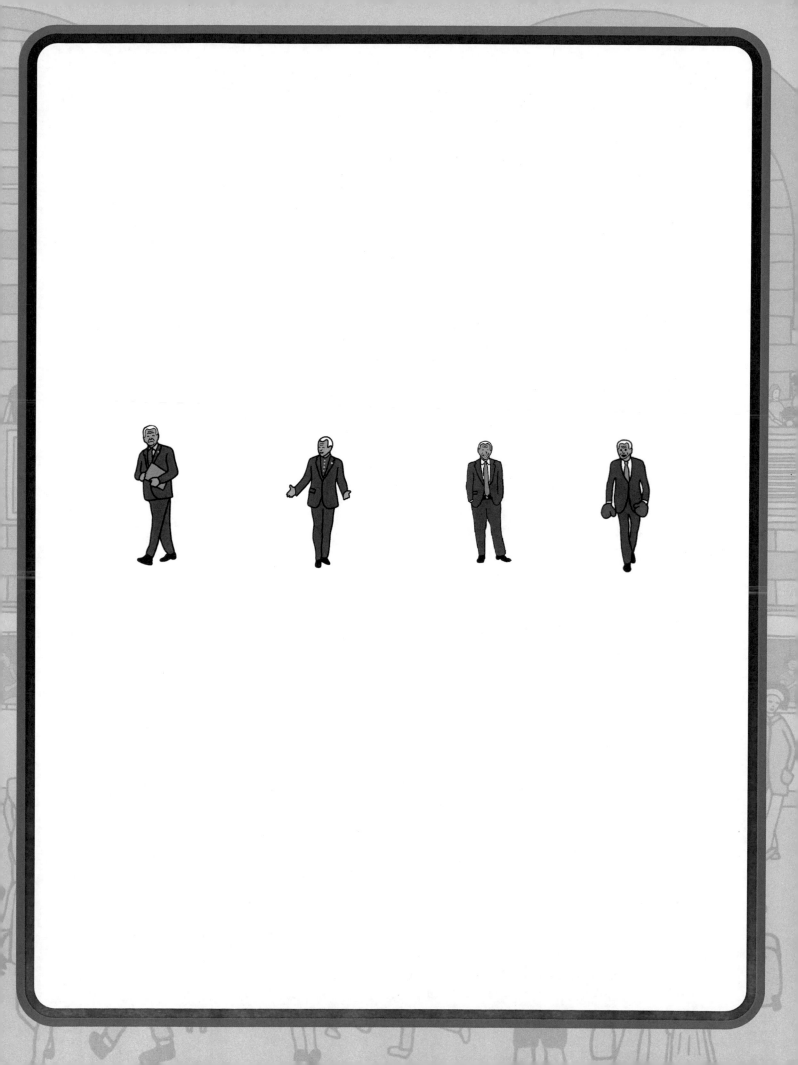

Amtrak Joe

Ol' Joe has gone by many nicknames throughout his political career, with new names appearing on a seemingly daily basis, but one that's really stood the test of time is Amtrak Joe. This is due to Biden riding the Amtrak to Washington, D.C. and back to his home in Delaware every day for 36 years - racking up around 2 million miles travelled on Amtrak, the equivalent of four years of his life. The Wilmington Amtrak station was hence named after him in 2011, so it's fair to say that Biden knows this place like the back of his hand. Good luck findin' him!

White House

The White House is one of busiest social hubs in Washington, accustomed to hosting up to five events per day ranging from meetings with dignitaries and VIPs, to smaller luncheons or private dinners. However, this is a particularly eventful day, as Trump is holding the 4th of July event at the White House. Needless to say, Joe Biden was not invited. However, ol' Joe doesn't want to miss this one as he knows the President throws the best parties. He's also confident he can get away with it, just as long as he can remember those hiding spots he found during his eight years there as VP.

Land of Bedfordshire

Sleepy Joe arrived at the Land of Bedfordshire, a place he knows only too well. Many have made fun of his sleepy demeanour, but little do people know that this is where Ol' Joe goes to get strategic advice for his campaign. He's currently looking for the Magical Dream Wizard, with hopes that he can help prepare him for his first debate with President Trump. However, he has lost his pyjama hat, and cannot return to the real world without it...

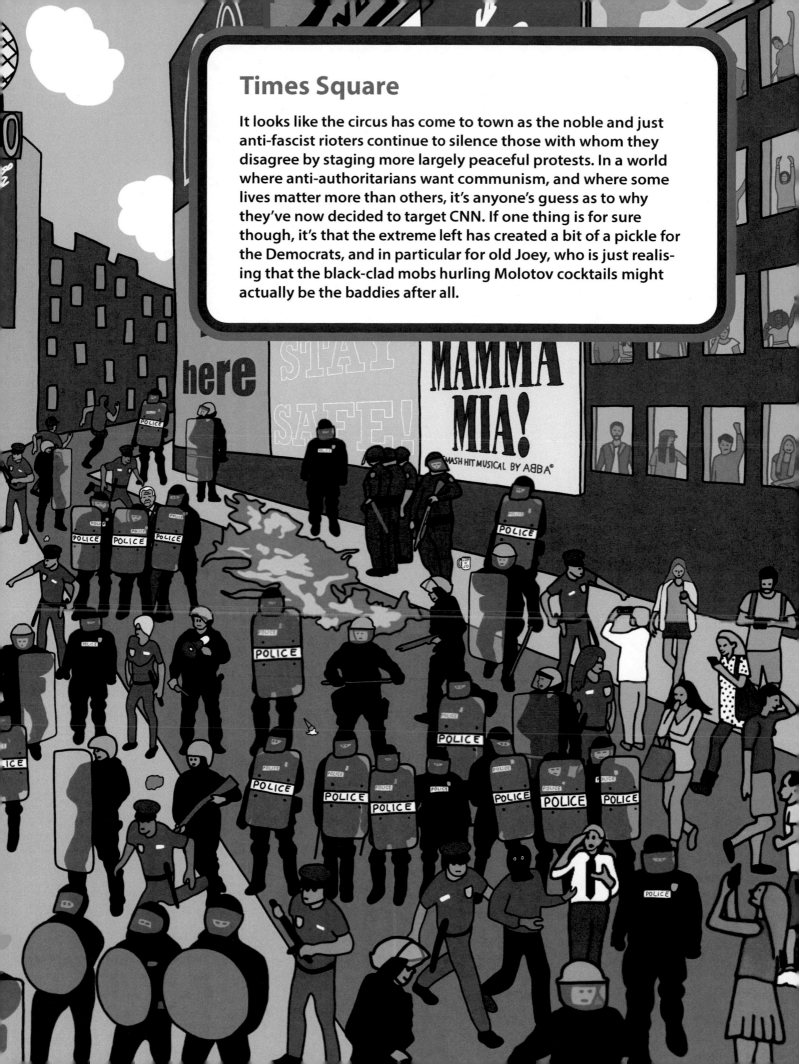

Times Square

It looks like the circus has come to town as the noble and just anti-fascist rioters continue to silence those with whom they disagree by staging more largely peaceful protests. In a world where anti-authoritarians want communism, and where some lives matter more than others, it's anyone's guess as to why they've now decided to target CNN. If one thing is for sure though, it's that the extreme left has created a bit of a pickle for the Democrats, and in particular for old Joey, who is just realising that the black-clad mobs hurling Molotov cocktails might actually be the baddies after all.

Supreme Court

In 2016 when Antonin Scalia passed away, Ol' Joe said "It is the President's constitutional duty to fill the Supreme Court seat", along with starting the hashtag #DoYourJob. Now that justice Ruth Bader Ginsberg has passed away, it seems Joe Biden and the democrats have taken a U-turn on this position, demanding Senator Mitch McConnel to forget and do the opposite of what they said in 2016. Can you find Joe in the partisan battle over the Supreme Court?

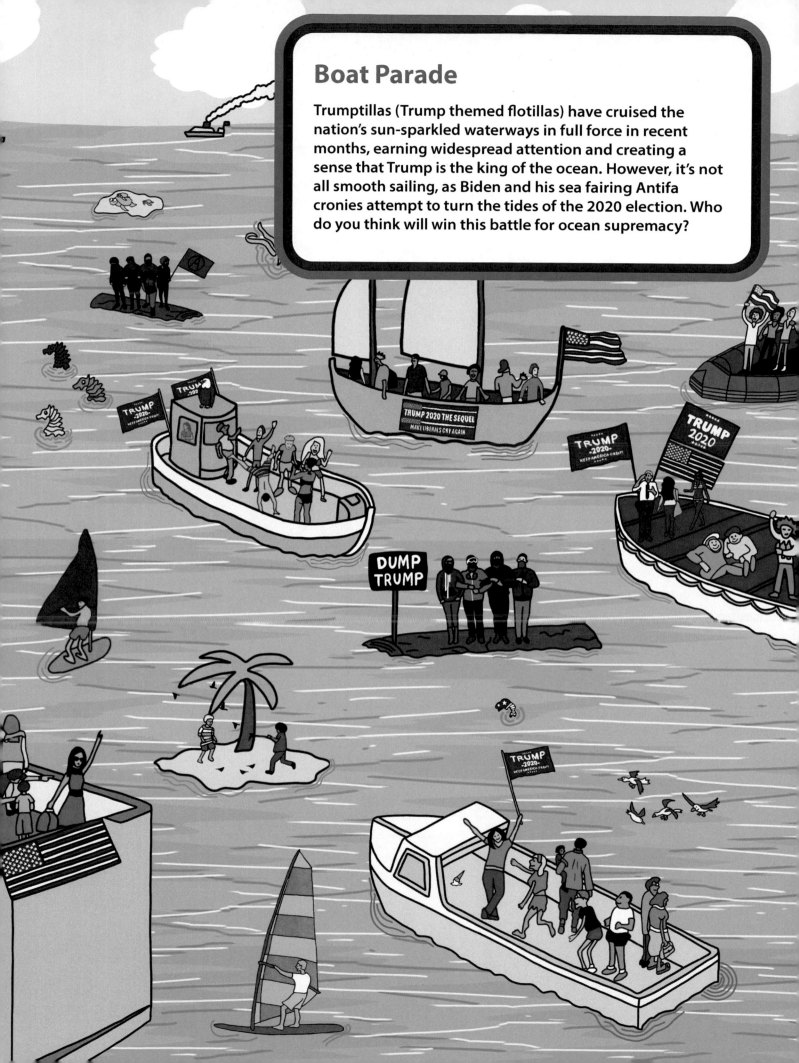

Boat Parade

Trumptillas (Trump themed flotillas) have cruised the nation's sun-sparkled waterways in full force in recent months, earning widespread attention and creating a sense that Trump is the king of the ocean. However, it's not all smooth sailing, as Biden and his sea fairing Antifa cronies attempt to turn the tides of the 2020 election. Who do you think will win this battle for ocean supremacy?

Wrestling Ring

Ol' Joe once said he would beat the hell out of President Trump if they were in high school. However, Trump loves a bit of one-to-one combat, with wrestling being his all-time favourite. Unfortunately for Joe, Trump has since made the Presidency his wrestling ring, and he's ready to duke it out with Biden and settle this election once and for all.

Beach

We'll fight them at the beaches! Well, when it comes to the beach, even presidential candidates need to stop the fighting to soak their shirtless old bones in the sea. And during these hard-economic times, you can count on Ol' JoJo to give you the shirt off his back.

Hint: You'll find 3 secret service agents chillin' close by.

If you
enjoyed Finding Biden,
please consider leaving a review
on Amazon.

C'mon Man!

Other books published by idiocratea:

Overheard at Waitrose
Overheard at Whole Foods
Google Search Poetry
Milk and Brexit

Made in the USA
Coppell, TX
19 December 2022

90227746R00019